love you
michael x

LESSONS FROM LIFE

After the Divorce

MICHAIAH DOMINGUEZ, MHC

After the Divorce

Disclaimer

This book is not intended to replace sound, personalized, professional counsel. It is to be utilized as an enrichment tool in conjunction with holistic methods of care. In no way does the author intend for the journal to address abuse of any kind or traumatic experiences that may have taken place prior to marriage, during marriage, or post-divorce. Neither the author nor publisher assume any liability for possible adverse consequences as a result of the contents herein.

" There is no time for despair, no place for self-pity, no need for silence, no room for fear. We speak. We write."

-Toni Morrison

Contents

Introduction
Page 01

Section I: Love & Marriage
Page 07

Section II: Looking Back
Page 25

Section III: Sorting Emotion
Page 47

Section IV: Self-Love
Page 63

Section V: Living Single
Page 75

Section VI: The Takeaways
Page 99

Conclusion
Page 127

Introduction

Relationships are one of the most crucial components of a fulfilling, successful life. They have an incredible power to build and sustain us. The right relationships foster a healthy sense of accomplishment and can be a source of great joy and pride. Our sense of self is largely defined by our relationships with others personally, professionally, culturally, and spiritually. Which is why divorce and marital separation are considered by many studies to be among the top three most distressing human experiences to suffer.

So, what happens when one of the most significant relationships in our lives fails? Simply put... it's gut wrenching. Our self-concept is challenged when a marriage ends because we interpret it in a number of damaging ways. Along with a broken heart and broken expectations is a trail of existential questions that ultimately have us wondering "Who am I now?" and "Where do I go from here?". Those unanswered questions leave us fumbling with some of these distorted beliefs...

Divorce as a reflection of self-worth

Self-worth is your sense of value as an individual. How you evaluate and assess your worth has implications on how you esteem yourself, the nature of how you perceive yourself, and the way in which you navigate decision making. The thoughts and beliefs you hold about yourself influence how you honor and care for yourself and others. It is the foundation of the extent to which you define your worthiness of love, respect, and compassion.

This oftentimes becomes compromised when a marriage goes awry. If your spouse (the one who vowed to deem you as worthy until death do us part and through sickness and health) no longer believes you are worthy of that commitment, naturally, you may struggle to hold steadfast to a healthy perception of self.

Feelings of rejection

In regards to divorce rejection can be understood as an abandonment of sorts; interpreted as a disregard for your invested time, attention, and affection. Or can be experienced as indifference and detachment from what was once so precious. You may even feel that rejection comes as the dismissing of your feelings of hurt, betrayal, or yearning to make things right.

Feelings of rejection insult our mental and emotional wellbeing. It's off putting nature is a devastating blow to the ego that can consume even the most confident of us. Rejection has the potential to deteriorate our sense of self-worth and lead to further isolation and loneliness if we allow it.

Inaccurate assessment of our personal success or failure

We live in a culture that is preoccupied with the appearance of success and the fear of failure. Which leaves little room to embrace valuable experiences that do not have an outcome of neither success nor failure. Divorce is one of those monumental occurrences that can be a pain point or a positive pivot depending on how it is processed. It simply cannot be categorized in one classification or the other.

Either way, your experiences of eventual success or failure in one area of your life cannot determine your inherent value as a human being. An unsuccessful marriage does not define you as a failure. Your identity is not based in any singular event of your life journey, no matter how significant it may be. Not even divorce.

Tremendous sense of loss

When entering into marriage, we have hopes and vision for what the future will hold. Be it a luxurious condo in New York City or an acre of land in Pennsylvania with a son, a daughter and a dog, we have presupposed notions of what our lives will look like 5, 10, and even 25 years from now. The end of a marriage marks the loss of not only what was, but also the collapse of all you had hoped for in your life as a couple.

The loss experienced in divorce is multifaceted. It includes the physical absence of your spouse, the tearing apart of your marriage and family, and the shattered expectations for the future. Most distressing of all, is the loss of the parts of you that no longer exist. Divorce may feel like a major part of who you are as a person is gone.

Good grief

Identifying grief as a component of divorce can make all the difference in how you are able to heal. Naming the grief helps to normalize the diverse symptoms of both good and bad days- fluctuating mood, emotional numbness, physical manifestations, feelings of despair and eventual hope. There are five stages of grief.[1]

Denial- the refusal to acknowledge the loss as reality
Anger- the combative opposition of facing the loss
Bargaining- negotiating to somehow arrive at a different outcome
Depression- the sorrowful feelings that accompany loss, and
Acceptance- willingness to integrate the loss as part of your reality and the will to live on

Good grief is the ability to navigate the stages (not in any particular order) with self-awareness and self-compassion that ultimately lead to an evolved understanding of the loss. In the process you acquire a radical acceptance of self, beyond the experience of loss, to actualize your potential to the fullest.

---

[1] Kubler-Ross, E., & Kessler, D. (2005) *On Grief and Grieving: Finding the Meaning of Grief Through the Five Stages of Loss. New York ; Toronto: Scribner.*

With a whole and healed self as the ultimate goal in mind, it is important to give your pain a voice. Sit with your set of circumstances. Observe and assess the significance you have ascribed to the memories of your marriage and divorce. What stories have you told yourself about how it all went down? What roles have you assigned to yourself and your ex? How have you been impacted, hindered, or helped by these stories?

Story 1: It wasn't my fault

One of the stories we tell ourselves is that we are not the ones at fault. We can pinpoint all of the reasons why the marriage failed and every reason traces back to the actions of our partner.

Although our partner may have committed atrocities in the relationship, assigning fault strips us of the ability to be self-reflective. No, you can never be to blame for someone else's actions. In no way do you deserve poor treatment, mishandling, infidelity, or any form of betrayal from the one you entrusted your heart to.

However, maintaining the "it's not my fault" story will perpetuate a victim mindset or a pity perspective that will harm you in the long run. Healing the hurt is our responsibility even when it is not our fault. In our divorce journey, we are gifted with the opportunity to take ownership of our boundaries (or lack thereof), evaluate our attachment and communication style, and take a look at our beliefs and behaviors that have contributed to our marital dynamic in one way or another. *

Story 2: I don't want to let go

Another story we could tell ourselves is that we are the ones who held on. This story is birthed mainly of two underlying desires. The first being the dissociation of guilt... the disconnection from the bad-guy burden.

As long as we assume the role of the spouse who desperately tried to make it work, we can freely charge our partner with the weight of responsibility for the dissolving of the marriage. Leaving ourselves blameless as it all comes tumbling down.

The second, is the devastating realization that you see potential in the marriage that your spouse no longer sees. You genuinely desire to persevere through whatever hardships have wedged between you and your spouse. Regardless of the circumstances or who is at fault, you are utterly committed to seeing your vows through. To your despair no matter how much you try to hold on, after time you realized that there was nothing left.

In either case, releasing the "I don't want to let go" story frees you so that you can create fulfillment through other meaningful situations and relationships. Once you let go, you are no longer availing yourself to prolonged pain and sorrow.

This does not include abuse of any kind- mental, emotional, financial, spiritual, physical, or sexual. The person who has committed the abusive act(s) is solely responsible for the misuse of power and control.

The divorce journey has given you the opportunity to love yourself deeply and passionately without the dependency on someone else's desire to invest in a continued relationship.

Story 3: I'm the bad guy

The right decision isn't always an easy decision. Being honest about your marriage, as you experience it, is both liberating and frightening. Divorce is painful even if you were the one who made the difficult choice to take action and end the marriage. The bad guy story can leave you riddled with guilt and shame as you assume responsibility for the consequences that you, your spouse, children, family and friends must endure.

Releasing the bad guy story frees you from being a moral prisoner of religious and cultural expectations, as well as societal constructs, that dictate to you that staying is the right thing to do. You are honoring yourself by acknowledging your true needs and taking strides to support your mental and emotional wellness.

The divorce journey has gifted you with the opportunity to release the guilt associated with putting yourself first. You have full permission to desire growth and seek self-actualization outside of the confines of marriage. You are no longer stunted, but are free to stand in your truth and create a life of intention, joy, and purpose.

If you made choices you regret and if you've terribly hurt your spouse because you are indeed the one who severed the trust, releasing the bad guy story frees you and them to consider forgiveness. Distancing yourselves from the marriage provides opportunity to heal because it allows space and time to identify, acknowledge and take responsibility for your actions. The damage can then be fully assessed and addressed. Self-awareness and personal growth can take place exponentially after a divorce as you take an honest look within yourself about your decisions and actions.

Can this guided journal really help?

Confronting your circumstances and taking inventory of your beliefs and fears is a powerful way to transform a painful event into a purposeful one. When you are intentional about fully processing a divorce, you redirect negative energy and take empowering, deliberate steps toward your healing. An important part of divorce recovery is reimagining and reestablishing your identity and self-worth. A key to doing that successfully is asking the right questions to extract the lessons that can be used in posturing yourself for what could be the greatest season of your life.

Surprisingly, journaling alone with a traditional free-write approach, actually does more harm than good. Aimlessly filling pages with disappointments, traumatic events, your most heartfelt brokenness and rage, only gives you license to further sulk in your distress. Potentially making a difficult situation worse. These guided journal prompts provide space for proper interpretation of the meaning of those memories.

The prompts offer guided introspection, much needed reflection, and an opportunity to perceive yourself and the divorce in fundamentally different and new ways.

Moreover, there is power in the pen. Transcribing your thoughts onto paper is one of the richest ways to determine significance and demonstrate appreciation for your thoughts and beliefs. Words never die. It is crucial that you evaluate the impact of the words you've been told about yourself, and to further explore the influence of words you've internalized concerning marriage and divorce. Most importantly, you've got to harness and harvest your authority concerning the weight of words that you tell yourself.

In this journal, I am asking that you take an honest look at those thoughts and beliefs... spending some time in what may be uncomfortable territory. We'll explore your fears, your defenses and where they may come from. We'll unveil your hopes and greatest expectations for your future. By the time you complete this journal, my desire is that you move toward a story of resilience and growth.

May your lessons from life lead you to realize that there is abundance, newness, and rebirth after the divorce.

Love &
Marriage

What examples of marriage did you have throughout your life?

How would you describe those marriages? Healthy, happy or something else? How do you know?

_____

_____

_____

_____

_____

_____

_____

_____

_____

_____

_____

_____

_____

_____

_____

_____

_____

_____

_____

_____

_____

_____

How have those relationships shaped your expectation of marriage?

_____

_____

_____

_____

_____

_____

_____

_____

_____

_____

_____

_____

_____

_____

_____

_____

_____

_____

_____

_____

_____

_____

_____

A *marriage personality* describes how a couple interacts with one another. It is not one spouse's characteristics that defines the *marriage personality* but, instead, it is how the two present as one.

Here are some examples.

a) Fun Loving- *Friendship and laughter is at the forefront of this marriage personality. Engaging with others by entertaining, traveling, or attending events is what keeps this marriage flourishing.*

b) Adventurous- *This marriage is thrill seeking and unconventional. Activities may include experimenting with new foods, camping, skydiving, or relocating. Trying new things together is what keeps this marriage flourishing.*

c) Trusting- *This marriage is based on integrity, honesty, and other fundamental moral pillars. Using this as a guide, there is deep connection and trust. Safety is what keeps this marriage flourishing.*

d) Entrepreneurial- *This marriage recognizes the goals and strength of each spouse. Together, they work diligently to see each other's dreams come to life. Purpose is what keeps this marriage flourishing.*

e) Nurturing- *This marriage is a haven of comfort and encouragement that supports healing and security. Peace, harmony, and affirmation of each other's needs is what keeps this marriage flourishing.*

f) Intimate- *This marriage fosters deep connection. Spiritual, sexual, and emotional vulnerability is what keeps this marriage flourishing.*

g) Unfaithful- *This marriage has suffered infidelity by one or both spouses. Unresolved betrayal leads to a cycle of distrust, guilt, and unforgiveness.*

h) Dishonest- *This marriage's main ingredient is secrecy. Lies by omission and commission keep the couple from fully knowing or trusting each other.*

i) Tumultuous- *This marriage struggles to communicate effectively. Constant disagreements, arguments, and silent treatment erupts throughout the marriage and often results in "walking on eggshells".*

j) Distant- *This marriage is disconnected. Neither friendship nor intimacy live in this marriage because the couple has (un)intentionally given up on closeness. Daily routines and responsibilities are priority.*

k) Picture Perfect- *This marriage's main concern is image. Beyond the presentation, the couple is void of connection and happiness. This facade is believable and appears as "couple goals".*

l) Abusive- *This marriage is more than unhealthy; it has crossed into physical, emotional, financial, or sexual abuse. Ultimately, an imbalance of power has been created to maintain control and to manipulate in extremely harmful ways.*

How would you describe your previous marriage's personality?

Which marriage personality is closest to your ideal?

_____

_____

_____

_____

_____

_____

_____

_____

_____

_____

_____

_____

_____

_____

_____

_____

_____

_____

_____

_____

_____

_____

_____

What were the barriers that kept you from creating a marriage that is more like your ideal? How did both you and your spouse contribute to those barriers?

What did you enjoy most about marriage?

What was most challenging for you?

What example did you want to model to your children through marriage?

How can your divorce leave a legacy of lessons for your children?

Take some time to reflect on
any additional beliefs, hopes,
or expectations you had about
love and marriage

I invite you to use this space to create a visual representation of love and marriage. Draw, sketch, use magazine clippings, or any crafty idea you'd like.

Looking
Back

If you were able to sit face to face with your ex and speak without interruption or fear, what feedback would you give to describe how you felt as their partner?

_____

_____

_____

_____

_____

_____

_____

_____

_____

_____

_____

_____

_____

_____

_____

_____

_____

_____

_____

_____

_____

_____

_____

_____

What feedback have you received from them about how they experience(d) you?

What, of that feedback, is based in truth? From your perspective, what areas have you self-identified as areas for improvement?

_____

_____

_____

_____

_____

_____

_____

_____

_____

_____

_____

_____

_____

_____

_____

_____

_____

_____

_____

_____

_____

_____

_____

_____

_____

What were your most proud contributions to the marriage?

Where did you show up in integrity as your most authentic self?

What have you learned about yourself through the transition from marriage to divorce?

What was revealed about how you respond to times of intense stress or uncertainty?

What are the ways of coping you have used to manage stress and uncertainty? Circle all that apply.

Holding yourself accountable   Establishing boundaries   Isolating/building walls

Placing blame   Denial   Connecting with family/friends

Reactivity   Exploring new interests/hobbies   Career projects/trainings

Increased substance use   Aligning with spiritual beliefs   Sexual activity/inactivity

Therapy   Mismanagement of money   Change in eating habits

Other(s)_____

_____

In what ways have these coping mechanisms been helpful for you or harmful to you?

_____

_____

_____

_____

_____

_____

_____

_____

_____

_____

_____

_____

_____

_____

_____

_____

What do you most regret?

What lessons have you learned from those regrets?

What strengths did you develop throughout the course of the marriage?

Trustworthiness/Honesty   Determination   Confidence   Gratitude

Flexibility   Patience   Effective Communication   Humility

Discipline   Dedication   Nurturance   Compassion

Spontaneity   Wisdom   Independence/Resourcefulness   Courageousness

Other(s)_____

_____

What can be done differently now with your new strengths and knowledge gained from your missteps?

Have you had to deal with any stigma associated with divorce? How so?

Have you experienced guilt or shame around the dissolving of your marriage?

Guilt is the acknowledgement of a choice or behavior that has impacted others. Shame is when that guilt shapes how you define yourself and influences how you feel about yourself.

_____

_____

_____

_____

_____

_____

_____

_____

_____

_____

_____

_____

_____

_____

_____

_____

_____

_____

_____

_____

How can you incorporate self-forgiveness to release guilt and shame?

Take some time to reflect on
the additional observations
you had about your marriage
that you realize in retrospect

Sorting Emotions

How would you describe your emotional experience post-separation? Select the image that best represents you and tell me more.

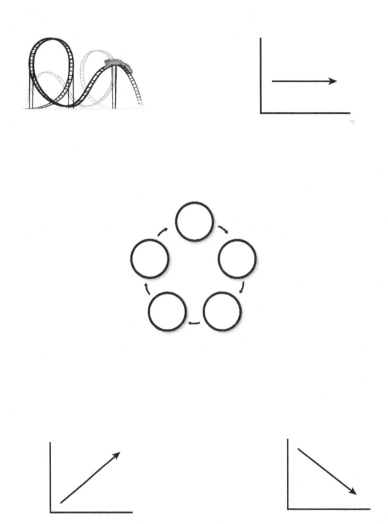

Feelings that have gone unseen, unheard, or unresolved are often the root of anger. Anger is a secondary emotion that stems from a primary unmet need. Here is a list of some common primary emotions that could result in anger.

Fear	Anxiety	Frustration	Confusion
Sadness	Isolation	Guilt	Shame
Jealousy	Helplessness	Hopelessness	Stress
Embarrassment	Rejection	Lonelines	Disappointment

Select the ones that resonate with you, or create your own, and enter them into the diagram.

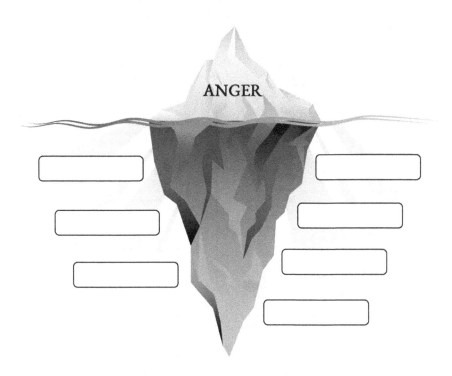

Which of the primary emotions are most sensitive for you?

What circumstances led to the emotions that lie beneath the surface?

In what ways can you show self-compassion for the experiences that brought you pain?

How did you most often communicate your primary emotional needs and/or
anger?

Will you continue to communicate your emotional needs this way or make some adjustments? Why?

Take some time to journal significant emotional milestones in your life and marriage

I invite you to use this space to create a visual representation of your emotional experience and growth. Draw, sketch, use magazine clippings, or any crafty idea you'd like.

Self
Love

How do you receive love? In order of importance from primary (1) to least important (5), rate your five love languages.[2]

_____Words of Affirmation

This language values love expressed with words. Verbal compliments and encouragement, both spoken and written, have the greatest impact. Negative or insulting comments really hurt if this is your love language.

_____Quality Time

This language values undivided attention. Whether it is a night on the couch or a couples vacation, the time is solely dedicated to the relationship with no distractions. Cancelled or postponed dates are devastating if this is your love language.

_____Receiving Gifts

This language values meaningful and thoughtful gifts. Expressing love through tokens of appreciation have the greatest impact for you. This can include luxurious items and also includes picking up a favorite snack after a long day of work.

_____Acts of Service

This language believes that "actions speak louder than words". Thoughtful and kind acts executed with a happy heart have the greatest impact. Acting out of obligation or with bitter tone really hurt if this is your love language.

_____Physical Touch

This language values physical displays of connection. Safety and intimacy through hand holding, kissing, hugging, etc. have the greatest impact. Emotional closeness is fostered by physical closeness.

Further describe the ways you receive love...

_____

_____

_____

_____

_____

_____

---

[2] Chapman, G. D. (1995). *The Five Love Languages: How to Express Heartfelt Commitment to Your Mate.* Chicago: Northfield Pub.

Have you ever considered loving yourself in the ways you've desired for others to love you? What action steps can you take to love yourself best?

Here are some suggestions to help you get started...

Words of Affirmation- *Keep a gratitude jar, recite affirmations, write positive post-it notes and stick them around your home*

_____

_____

_____

Quality time- *Schedule a date with yourself to watch the sun rise or set, paint or craft, watch your favorite show*

_____

_____

_____

Receiving Gifts- *Invest in your hobbies, treat yourself to a gift each pay period, join a subscription box service*

_____

_____

_____

Acts of Kindness- *Declutter your space, meal prep for the week, set weekly goals*

_____

_____

_____

Physical Touch- *Stretch or exercise, take baths, invest in skin care or hair care*

_____

_____

_____

Self-care is one way to express self-love. A component of wholehearted self-care is the exploration of what hinders us from experiencing the fullness of exceedingly abundant self-love.

Complete the reflection exercise to describe your experience and functioning in each area.

Self-criticism

_____
_____
_____
_____

Negative
self-talk

_____
_____
_____
_____

Self-doubt

_____
_____
_____

Negative
body image

_____
_____
_____

Self-love:
What does it mean to
me?

_____
_____
_____
_____
_____
_____
_____

_____
_____
_____
_____
_____
_____

In what ways will you implement self-care for improved overall wellness? [3]

- **Physical wellness-** *Includes your physical health, nutrition, healthy sleep patterns, and sexual wellness*

  _____

  _____

  _____

  _____

- **Occupational wellness-** *Includes your satisfaction with career and educational goals*

  _____

  _____

  _____

  _____

- **Spiritual wellness-** *Includes your sense of purpose, connectivity, and meaning for life*

  _____

  _____

  _____

  _____

- **Social wellness-** *Includes a sense of belonging, support, and healthy interpersonal relationships*

  _____

  _____

  _____

  _____

---

[3] Swarbrick, M. (2006). A Wellness Approach. *Psychiatric Rehabilitation Journal,* 29(4), 311-314

- **Financial wellness-** *Includes financial knowledge, satisfaction, stability, and growth*

  _____

  _____

  _____

  _____

- **Emotional wellness-** *Includes being able to maintain, cope, and thrive in life and in relationships*

  _____

  _____

  _____

  _____

- **Environmental wellness-** *Includes occupying pleasant and stimulating physical and emotional environments*

  _____

  _____

  _____

  _____

- **Intellectual wellness-** *Includes recognizing creative and knowledge-based abilities*

  _____

  _____

  _____

  _____

In what ways will you incorporate rest and play in order to enjoy your singleness to the fullest?

- **Recreation-** *scheduling time to participate in something fun*

  _____

  _____

  _____

- **Escape-** *incorporating music, entertainment, travel or reading into your regular routine*

  _____

  _____

  _____

- **Relaxation-** *creating "down-time" where you intentionally put away your to-do list*

  _____

  _____

  _____

- **Spirituality-** *incorporating meditation, prayer, gratitude, and/or silence to honor your spirit*

  _____

  _____

  _____

- **Rest-** *breathe, nap, take it easy*

  _____

  _____

  _____

Take some time to consider how you will further fully commit to deepening self-love in thought and action

Living Single

What do you enjoy and appreciate most about your singleness?

What is most challenging about being single after marriage?

How would you describe your self-image throughout the course of the marriage? Feel free to write key words, sketch, diagram, or color within the space to best express your self image.

CAREER

INTELLIGENCE

GOAL SETTING/ACHIEVING

PARENTING

CONFIDENCE

PHYSICAL APPEARANCE

ABILITY

FINANCIAL FORTITUDE

SELF-WORTH

Has your self-image shifted post-separation? In what ways?

Career

During the marriage, I would describe myself as _____ .

Now, I would describe myself as _____ .

My self-image has/has not shifted in this area because _____

_____ .

I would say that I am pleased/satisfied/dissatisfied with the changes.

Moving forward I see myself _____

_____ .

I would further reflect that _____

_____

_____ .

Intelligence

During the marriage, I would describe myself as _____ .

Now, I would describe myself as _____ .

My self-image has/has not shifted in this area because _____

_____ .

I would say that I am pleased/satisfied/dissatisfied with the changes.

Moving forward I see myself _____

_____ .

I would further reflect that _____

_____

_____ .

Goal setting/achieving

During the marriage, I would describe myself as_____ .

Now, I would describe myself as _____ .

My self-image has/has not shifted in this area because _____

_____ .

I would say that I am pleased/satisfied/dissatisfied with the changes.

Moving forward I see myself _____

_____ .

I would further reflect that _____

_____

_____ .

Parenting

During the marriage, I would describe myself as_____ .

Now, I would describe myself as _____ .

My self-image has/has not shifted in this area because _____

_____ .

I would say that I am pleased/satisfied/dissatisfied with the changes.

Moving forward I see myself _____

_____ .

I would further reflect that _____

_____

_____ .

Confidence

During the marriage, I would describe myself as _____ .

Now, I would describe myself as _____ .

My self-image has/has not shifted in this area because _____

_____ .

I would say that I am pleased/satisfied/dissatisfied with the changes.

Moving forward I see myself _____

_____ .

I would further reflect that _____

_____

_____ .

Physical appearance

During the marriage, I would describe myself as _____ .

Now, I would describe myself as _____ .

My self-image has/has not shifted in this area because _____

_____ .

I would say that I am pleased/satisfied/dissatisfied with the changes.

Moving forward I see myself _____

_____ .

I would further reflect that _____

_____

_____ .

Ability

During the marriage, I would describe myself as_____ .

Now, I would describe myself as _____ .

My self-image has/has not shifted in this area because _____

_____ .

I would say that I am pleased/satisfied/dissatisfied with the changes.

Moving forward I see myself _____

_____ .

I would further reflect that _____

_____

_____ .

Financial fortitude

During the marriage, I would describe myself as_____ .

Now, I would describe myself as _____ .

My self-image has/has not shifted in this area because _____

_____ .

I would say that I am pleased/satisfied/dissatisfied with the changes.

Moving forward I see myself _____

_____ .

I would further reflect that _____

_____

_____ .

Self-worth

During the marriage, I would describe myself as _____ .

Now, I would describe myself as _____ .

My self-image has/has not shifted in this area because _____

_____ .

I would say that I am pleased/satisfied/dissatisfied with the changes.

Moving forward I see myself _____

_____ .

I would further reflect that _____

_____

_____ .

What strengths did you already have coming into the marriage? Highlight all that apply.

Trusting	Expressive	Confident	Good Listener
Loving	Honest	Supportive	Self-control
Authentic	Fun	Patient	Risk taking
Provider	Respected	Loving	Faithful
Nurturing	Curious	Sensual/sexual	Friend
Assertive	Compassionate	Forgiving	Protector
Curious	Decision-making	Encourager	Appreciative
Romantic	Giving	Content	Diligent
Hopeful	Resourceful	Joyful	

Go into detail and describe how you showed up.

_____

_____

_____

_____

_____

_____

_____

_____

_____

_____

_____

_____

_____

_____

_____

What strengths doubled as obstacles in your marriage?

What strengths will you continue to exhibit throughout your singleness?

How would you describe your feelings about a future relationship or current relationship status?

Fearful ☐   Excited ☐   Hopeful ☐   In pursuit ☐

Uninterested ☐   Already in a relationship ☐   Remarried ☐

Tell me more...

_____

_____

_____

_____

_____

_____

_____

_____

_____

_____

_____

_____

_____

_____

_____

_____

_____

_____

What non-negotiables and boundaries will you implement to maintain a healthy relationship?

Keep in mind, a non-negotiable is a fixed standard that if violated, will end a relationship immediately. A boundary is a standard that fosters safety and security within a relationship. Boundaries and non-negotiables are expectations that should be discussed and understood by both parties when establishing the foundation of a relationship.

_____

_____

_____

_____

_____

_____

_____

_____

_____

_____

_____

_____

_____

_____

_____

_____

_____

_____

_____

In what ways has your previous marriage influenced your non-negotiables and/or boundaries for future relationships?

_____

_____

_____

_____

_____

_____

_____

_____

_____

_____

_____

_____

_____

_____

_____

_____

_____

_____

_____

_____

_____

_____

While there will be healthy influences from lessons learned, these could also be established out of fear from repeating pain. Be clear and intentional about both.

What are some of the qualities you value in a future partner?

Do your very best to avoid writing what you *do not* want, and focus more on writing *what you are inviting into your next relationship.* Keep in mind, writing about physical attributes is nice but what's most important are the qualities that cannot be seen. How do you desire to be treated? How would you like to engage in day to day tasks? What type of compatibility are you looking for? That's what I'm talking about!

_____

_____

_____

_____

_____

_____

_____

_____

_____

_____

_____

_____

_____

_____

_____

_____

_____

_____

How would this partner complement your strengths? How could you complement each other?

_____

_____

_____

_____

_____

_____

_____

_____

_____

_____

_____

_____

_____

_____

_____

_____

_____

_____

_____

_____

_____

_____

_____

_____

_____

_____

Your happiness and fulfillment is not contingent upon the success of your next relationship. In what ways will you continue to reinforce your inner peace, joy, and security without dependency on a future partner?

Take some time to reflect on any additional thoughts or feelings you have about singleness post-divorce

The Takeaway

What are your beliefs about marriage now? How have they changed, if at all?

What are your greatest fears, if any, about being single?

What are your greatest fears, if any, about another relationship?

How will you intentionally address your fears and concerns?

What are the three biggest takeaways that you've learned throughout your marriage, divorce, and singleness?

Circle the phrase that best reflects your beliefs about change.

"The only lasting truth is change."
- Octavia Butler

"New beginnings are often disguised as painful endings." - Lao Tzu

"Change begins at the end of your comfort zone." - Roy T. Bennett

"Nothing is as painful to the human mind as a great and sudden change."
- Mary Wollstonecraft Shelley

"Incredible change happens in your life when you decide to take control of what you do have power over instead of craving control over what you don't."
- Steve Maraboli

Tell me more

_____

_____

_____

_____

_____

_____

_____

_____

_____

_____

_____

_____

_____

_____

_____

Reflect and scale yourself on the following statements about change.

I am optimistic about change.

☐ Always   ☐ Sometimes   ☐ Never

I am hesitant and/or fearful of change.

☐ Always   ☐ Sometimes   ☐ Never

I am prepared for change.

☐ Always   ☐ Sometimes   ☐ Never

I am aware of the ways divorce has changed me/my life.

☐ Yes   ☐ No

I am at peace with those changes.

☐ Yes   ☐ No

What are you most hopeful about as you move forward into an independent, healthy lifestyle?

Write three affirmations that will support you in harnessing hope, strength, and encouragement in the year to come.

Imagine yourself three years from now.

Visualize how you will look and feel. How will you have grown? What will you be doing?

What goals will you achieve?

Take some time to describe the life you desire. Be as detailed as possible.

Fast forward. What would your future self say to you today? Imagining that you are in your destined place in five years, write a letter to your current self.

Take some time to process final thoughts as your journaling comes to a close. What are some additional realizations you'd like to highlight?

I invite you to use this space as a vision board. Use magazine or newspaper clippings, pictures, stickers and more to create a visual representation of your desires, dreams, and goals for the coming year.

Conclusion

So, what now?

This journal is a compelling look into significant vignettes of your marriage and divorce. Reflecting on the words you've shared here will help you discover meaning and proper perspective. Take notice of recurring themes, the thread of beliefs that weave your story together. What patterns have you identified? How can you further learn from them in order to continue to mature? This current chapter is closed but your story is ever evolving. You have full permission and authority to take control of your life- influencing its evolution- by reclaiming your voice and declaring fresh, new beginnings. Write a new story!

Yes, you have gone through challenging times. At one point or another you have said or done things you may regret, you have faced moments of embarrassment, and have experienced a fair share of hurt. There are lessons in all of it...

You are not your shame

You are not your mistakes. You are not your problems. You are not a victim. You are not a villain. You are not wrong. You are not always right. You are not your anger. You are not your pain. You are not your insecurities. You are not a failure. You are not any of the labels you have assigned yourself. You are not the labels others have assigned to you. The divorce does not define you. The divorce cannot destroy you. You are human and you have one hell of a story to tell.

Power of choice to change the narrative

Being an autonomous individual, you have the ability to take ownership of your thoughts and actions regardless of external influences and circumstances. You also have the agency to become everything you are determined to be and the freedom to realize your fullest potential. The sooner you hold to this empowering concept, the sooner you will be able to confidently commit to personal decisions that will create a shift in the negative narrative.

There is meaning & purpose in the pain

Life is not happening to you but for you. All that you have been through will be used as an integral piece of your larger life story. Every lesson and loss will develop and strengthen you so that you can be used as a beacon of hope. As time passes and your healing journey continues, you will detach from the despair and begin to see meaning in every hardship and purpose in every tear. Like gold tried and perfected by fire, you will come out of this painful place gleaming and polished to walk boldly in your purpose.

Hope & great expectation

Your divorce journey has gifted you with the opportunity to take the limits off your expectations and ambitions. You may have restricted your blessings by designing them so strictly; constrained according to your limited understanding of your worth. Your dreams and vision for your life are not connected to or contingent upon any relationship outside of yourself. If you think that you cannot achieve your goals because of your marital status, think again. There is greatness in you. You are worthy of the life you want and the life you want is tangible and available to you. The story may not have unfolded the way you intended, but do not abandon your hope for your expected end. There is greater for you... even after the divorce.

Made in USA - North Chelmsford, MA
1199785_9780578773438
11.24.2020 1628